DRAW UNICORNS with SIMPLE SHAPES

by

Jo Moon

ARCTURUS

ARCTURUS

This edition published in 2019 by Arcturus Publishing Limited
26/27 Bickels Yard, 151–153 Bermondsey Street,
London SE1 3HA

Illustrator: Jo Moon
Author: Lisa Regan
Designer: Sarah Fountain

ISBN: 978-1-78950-532-0
CH007339NT
Supplier 29, Date 1019, Print run 8516

Printed in China

Contents

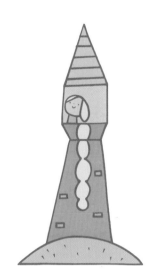

How to Use This Book

Have you ever read stories about magical creatures and wished you could draw your own? Well, now you can! We have made it really easy by breaking them down into basic shapes such as ovals and rectangles. Follow the steps to learn how to sketch a selection of lovable characters, and then draw them into the cute illustrated scenes.

Start each picture with step 1, adding new shapes at each step as highlighted.

Create glorious scenes by adding anything you have learned to draw.

Here are some of the shapes you will use.
Can you remember their names?

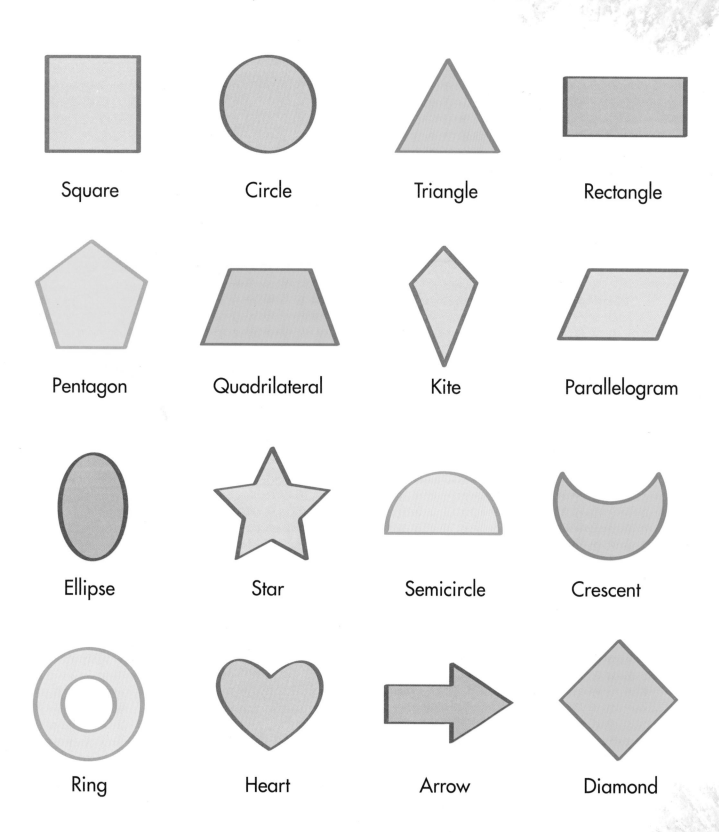

Square   Circle   Triangle   Rectangle

Pentagon   Quadrilateral   Kite   Parallelogram

Ellipse   Star   Semicircle   Crescent

Ring   Heart   Arrow   Diamond

Forest Friends

If you go down to the woods today, here are some of the characters you might meet! Learn how to draw a gorgeous unicorn, as well as a few other forest friends!

Page 14

Page 18

Page 12

Page 8

Page 7

Page 13

Page 11

Wood Nymph

Use shades of green so he can blend into his surroundings.

Woodland Unicorn

Use triangles for the legs, and for her magical horn, of course!

Fill this peaceful forest with beautiful unicorns and their friends.

Add more sprites playing happily together.

Sprite

This magical creature is doing a cartwheel!

Pixie

This little creature has ragged clothes and delicate wings.

Gnome

Have fun drawing this little fella with a BIG beard!

Brownie

Make sure you remember to draw this creature's cute, pointed ears!

Brownies mostly come out at night to help around the home.

Fill this fairy village with all kinds of woodland creatures.

Yeti Pup

How cute is this little guy? And he's super simple to draw.

Draw lots more yetis having fun in the snow.

Fairy Kingdom

Create a whole new kingdom filled with unicorns, dragons, and fairies flitting past. You can even make a fairy palace with a king and a queen to live in it!

Page 27

Page 24

Page 26

Page 22

Page 21

Page 34

Page 28

Page 33

Fairy

Give your fairy beautiful wings and a magical wand.

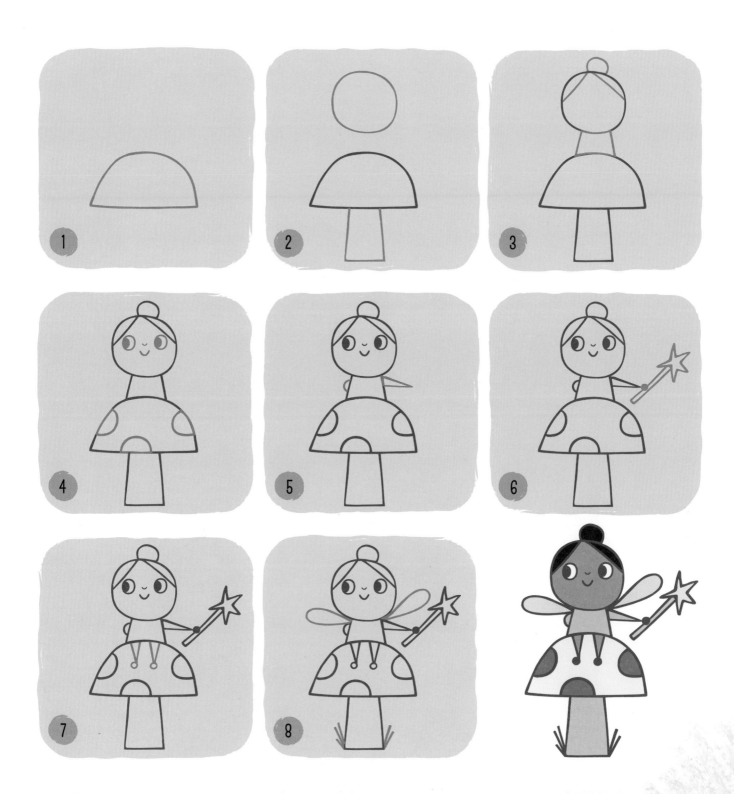

21

Fairy King

This royal ruler is very easy to draw.

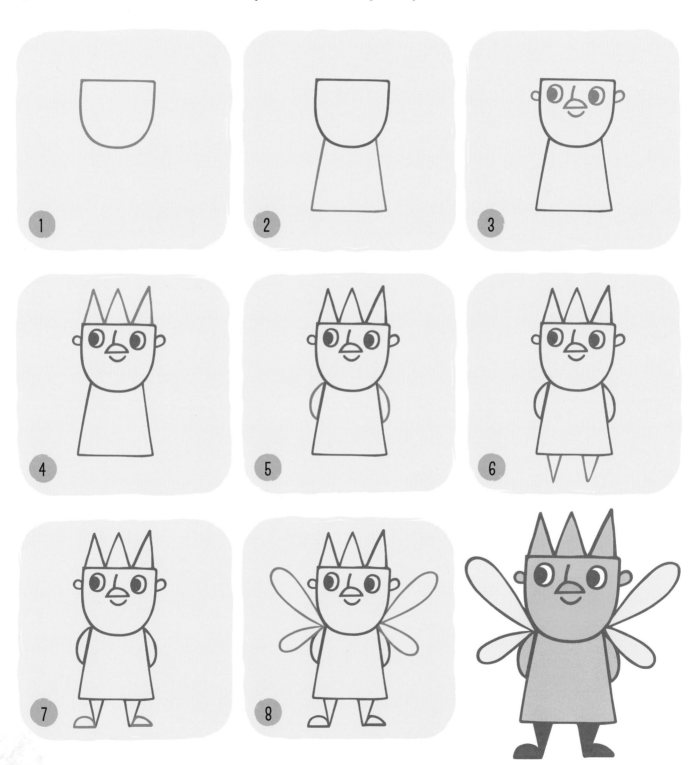

Draw the king in his throne room. Can you add the rest of the royal family?

23

Rainbow Unicorn

Look who has come to visit with her dazzling rainbow markings!

Add some more unicorn friends playing in the waterfall.

Jack Frost

He's a naughty imp, for sure! But he is great fun to draw.

Fairy Palace

Draw a home fit for the finest fairies.

Llamacorn

Everyone loves a llama, especially a magical one!

Add lots of leaping llamacorns to this sunny scene.

It is market day in Fairyland. Draw lots of fairies and their friends!

Giddy up! Add more unicorn-drawn carriages on the fairy highway.

Fairy Carriage

Join these simple shapes together for the perfect ride.

Snow Dragon

Here's a spiky character to draw. She's still adorable!

The mountains are home to lots of snow dragons. Add some more!

Under the Sea

Create your own enchanted underwater world, filled with mermaids, merkings, and their magical marine friends.

Page 42

Page 45

Page 48

Page 46

Page 41

Page 38

Page 37

Page 40

Sea Unicorn

How adorable is this creature? He's the perfect pet for a mermaid.

Mermaid

Use triangles and a crescent moon for her distinctive tail.

What will you call your mermaid? Draw her here with her friends.

Narwhal

This creature is SO simple, you will want to draw narwhals everywhere!

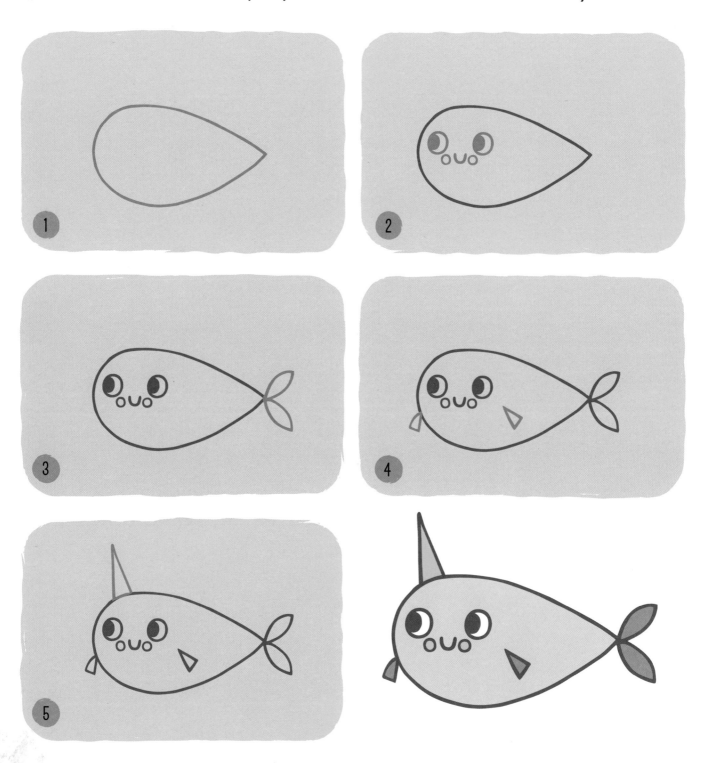

Sea Palace

Decorate this ocean dwelling with shells and seaweed.

Underwater King

This royal merman looks happy in his ocean home.

Who else is swimming in the underwater kingdom?

43

Mirror, mirror, make some magic and show me more little merprincesses.

Merprincess

She has the body of a fish, and beautiful, big round eyes.

Ocean-going Carriage

Start with a semicircle, to draw a carriage that will ride beneath the waves!

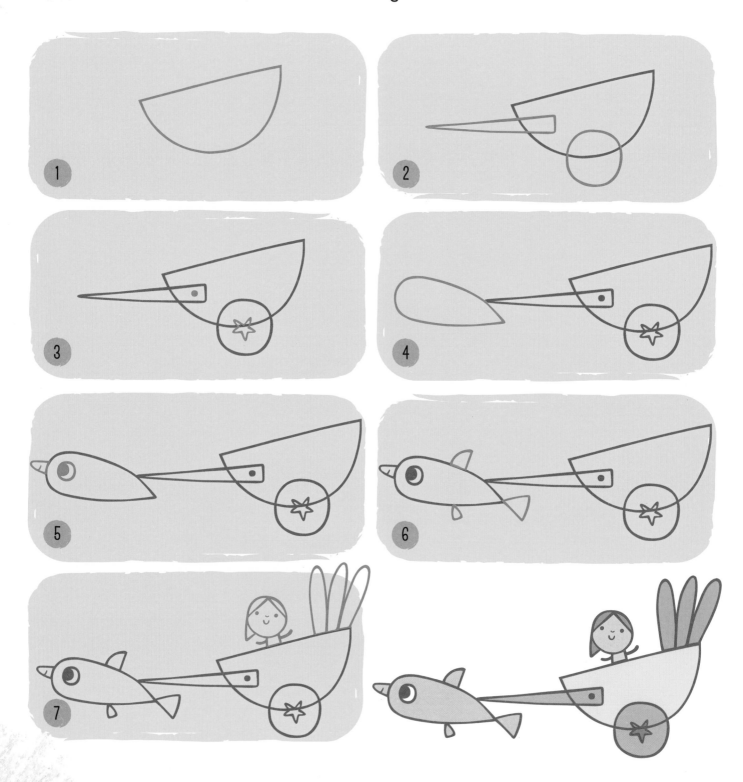

1

2

3

4

5

6

7

Who is the fastest? Draw a dolphin race to find out!

47

Purrmaid

Not all cats are afraid of water! This kitty loves it.

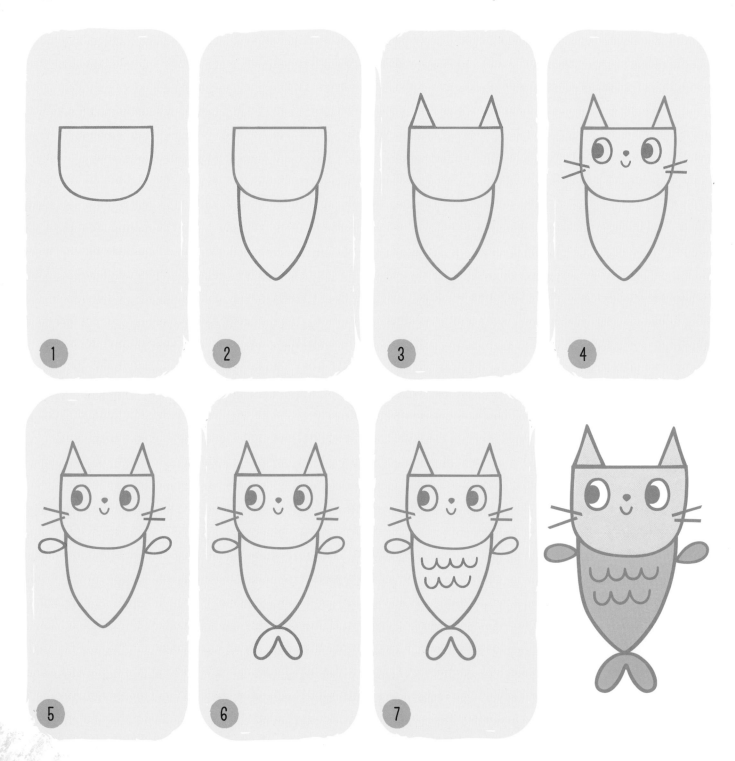

A purrmaid is so simple to draw. Fill this space with lots of them.

Who is shimmying around the shipwreck? You decide!

Tales of Enchantment

Learn how to draw some wonderful fairytale characters. Then let your imagination take over, and sketch amazing adventures of your own!

Page 59

Page 62

Page 58

Page 56

Page 64

Page 53

Page 54

Genie

Draw this genie as he magically appears from the lamp. Will he grant your wishes?

Dragon Baby

Big, round eyes make this little creature look super cute.

Draw a full fairytale scene here!

Friendly Dragon

Get this one right, and you can draw a whole family!

Can you give this little cutie some friends?

Troll

His round face and feet are guaranteed to make you smile.

Elf

Ooh, he's made a present! Draw some more, quick!

Who will you add to this wonderful fairytale world?

Knight on a Unicorn

Every knight needs a trusty steed to ride upon!

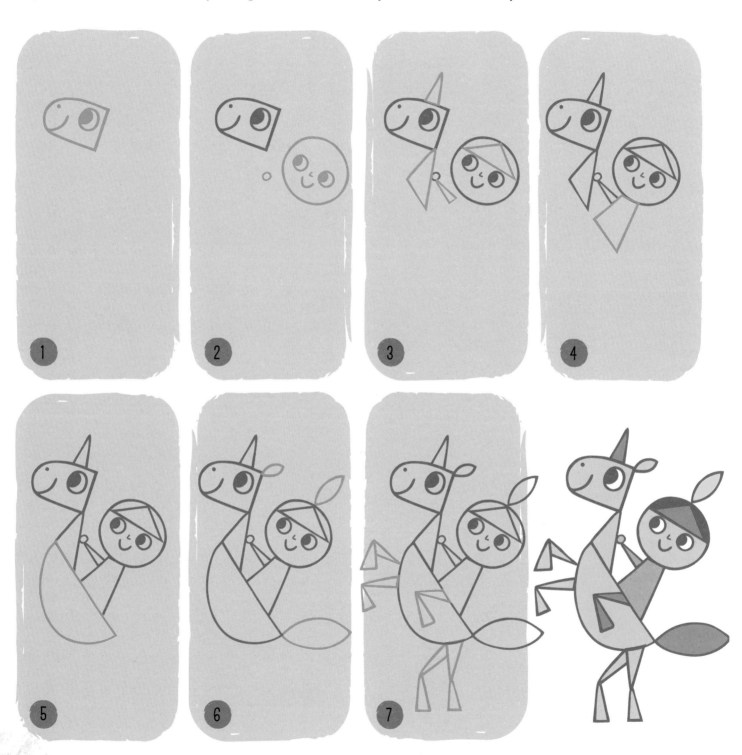

Add some more knights for this jousting tournament.

Griffin Chick

This creature has a lion's tail and an eagle's wings and beak.

Add more griffin chicks to this faraway fantasy place.

Flying High

Up, up, and away! Raise your eyes to the skies to see what fantastic creatures are flying up above.

Page 69

Page 70

Page 79

Page 80

Page 72

Page 67

Page 82

Page 76

Magic Carpet

Whisk your rider away to another world with this magical mat!

How many flying fairies can you fit here?

Flying Fairy

Draw a fairy with her wings spread, ready to fly and flutter!

Flying Dragon

This cute dragon has a horn on her head, just like a unicorn.

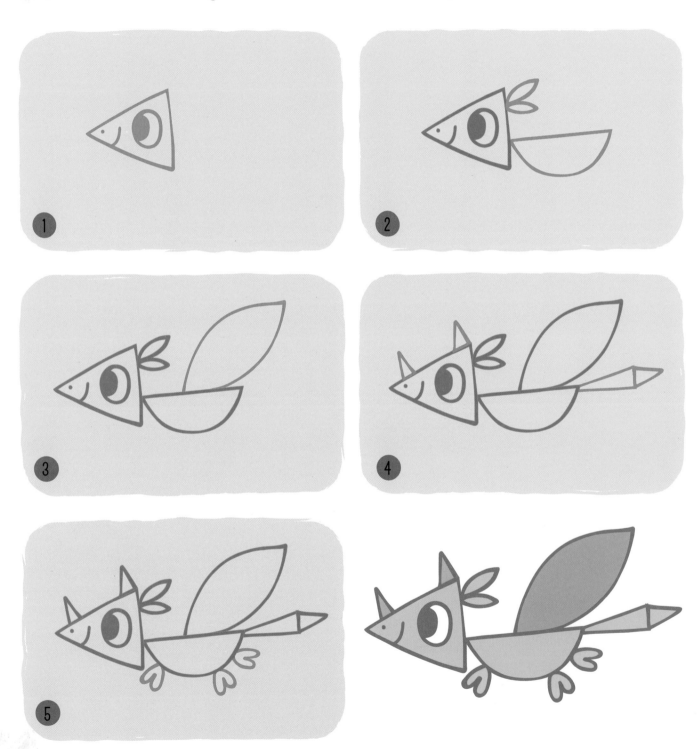

Add more dragons having fun in the clouds.

Phoenix

Learn to draw this mystical sunbird as it flies in to say hello.

Now give the phoenix some friends!

Fill the skies with lots of winged wonders!

Winged Unicorn

This flying unicorn has beautiful feathered wings.

Fly, fly over the land and the oceans!

Make this whole scene bright and lively!

Rainbow Dragon

Here's another dragon to draw, with all the shades of the rainbow.

Fire Dragon

This little dragon can breathe flames. Watch out!

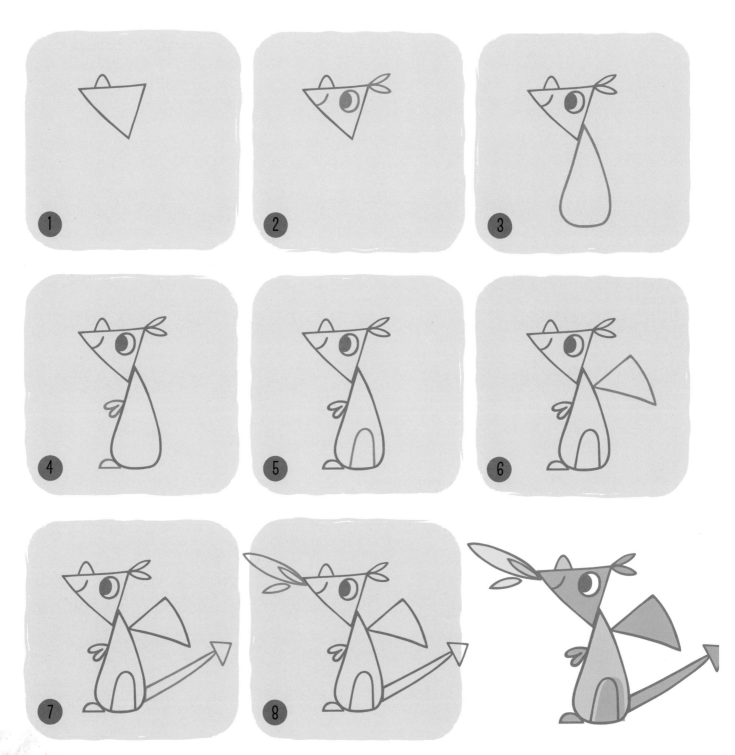

How many different dragons can you draw now?

Magical Deer

This wondrous creature is a deer with wings. How magical!

What other creatures could join your flying deer in the skies?

Princess Tales

What is better than learning how to draw a princess? Learning how to draw all kinds of different princesses!

Page 90

Page 96

Page 85

Page 88

Page 87

Page 93

Rapunzel Tower

What do you think Rapunzel can see from her tower?

This swan is the princess of the pond. Draw her some friends!

Swan Princess

The swan princess is made up of circles and semicircles. So simple!

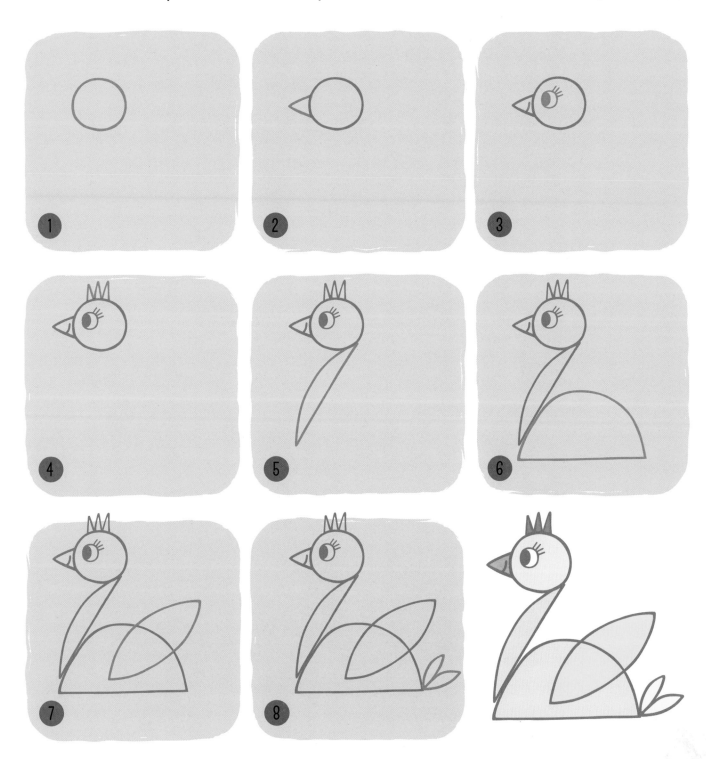

Princess Carriage

Draw the basic shape and then add your own decorations.

Let's go for a ride together!

Princess Palace

Every princess needs a royal dwelling.

Fill the palace gardens with fairies and flowers.

Add some more witches and watch them fly!

Friendly Witch

You'll need to draw lots of triangles to make this witch.

How many unicorns have gathered in this clearing in the forest?

Unicorn Princess

Bring together all you have learned, and create one wondrous final creature!